Differentiated Activities

Group/Independent work

BOOK 3

Sue Palmer
Michaela Morgan

Contents

Photocopy Masters

The Great Whatsit (*common and proper nouns*) 1

Alphie's Action Alphabet (*verbs*) 7

What the animals said (*powerful verbs*) 11

Past and Present (*tense*) 14

Knock knock! (*question and exclamation marks*) 20

The Seven Sentence Story (*sentences and sentence boundaries*) 23

Chatterbox (*direct speech punctuation*) 26

The Punctuation Times (*sentence punctuation*) 32

Adjectives for Sale! (*adjectives*) 38

Me and my Monster (*adjectives*) 41

Singular and Plural (*singular and plural*) 47

All Together Now! (*collective nouns*) 53

Chunky Comma to the Rescue! (*uses of the comma*) 57

The Capital Wall (*uses of capital letters*) 60

Teach Yourself Earth (*1st, 2nd and 3rd person agreement*) 63

The Village without Pronouns (*personal and possessive pronouns*) 66

Links are Us! (*conjunctions*) 70

Shrinking Violet (*time connectives*) 76

Name ....

The Great Whatsit

Change each whatsit to the correct noun.

Early one whatsit, the Great Whatsit was reading his whatsit,

when he noticed something exciting. "Buried whatsit," he said.

"That's interesting. Maybe we can solve this whatsit."

He got into his Whatsit and drove to Whatsit. Lots of whatsits

were already there looking for the buried whatsit. Some were

digging in the whatsit. Some were digging by the whatsit.

"Hmmm," said the Great Whatsit. "If you want

to find buried whatsit, you have to look in

the right whatsit. X marks the whatsit!"

place mystery treasure sea people Detective newspaper spot sand day Rolls Royce

Teaching objective: Y3 T1 S1 *common and proper nouns; grammatical awareness*

Name ....

The Great Whatsit

Change each whatsit to the correct noun.

One fine whatsit, Mrs Whatsit's whatsit visited the whatsit. They saw great big trumpeting whatsits, funny little flapping black and white whatsits and a big white polar whatsit.

Their favourites were the whatsits which climbed up tall whatsits and swung from long whatsits. One of them took Mrs Whatsit's whatsit!

Mrs Whatsit was very cross. "Someone get my whatsit back from that whatsit!" she shouted – but it was too late. The whatsit had eaten it!

Teaching objective: Y3 T1 S1 *common and proper nouns; grammatical awareness*

Big Book Grammar, Heinemann 2000. Copying permitted for purchasing school only. This material is not copyright free.

Name ....

The Great Whatsit

Change each whatsit to a noun that sounds right.

Once upon a whatsit there were three little whatsits. They were

called Whatsit, Whatsit and Whatsit. They all lived together in a

funny little whatsit. They were all afraid of the bad whatsit who

lived in the deep, dark whatsit.

One sunny whatsit the three whatsits went out walking in the

deep, dark whatsit. Suddenly the bad whatsit jumped out at

them. "What are you whatsits doing in my whatsit?" he growled.

"We're picking whatsits," the whatsits said.

"Give them to me!" roared the

whatsit. He took the whatsits from them

but the bunches of whatsits made him

sneeze. "Aaaachooo!" went the bad

whatsit and he sneezed so hard that

he fell backwards into the whatsit.

Teaching objective: Y3 T1 S1 *common and proper nouns; grammatical awareness*

Name ....

The Great Whatsit

Read the story. All the nouns are underlined. Write each noun in the correct box.

Mrs Watson was a little <u>lady</u> who had a big <u>dog</u>. It was called <u>Winston</u>. Every <u>Sunday</u> Mrs Watson took <u>Winston</u> to the <u>park</u> in <u>Newtown</u>. They went on the <u>swings</u>. They played in the <u>sand</u>. They slid on the <u>slide</u>. Then <u>Winston</u> took Mrs Watson <u>home</u>.

Proper nouns	*Common nouns*
Mrs Watson	dog

Teaching objective: Y3 T1 S1 *common and proper nouns; grammatical awareness*

Name ....

The Great Whatsit

Read the story. Underline all the nouns.
Write each noun in the correct box.

Danny Dazzle and Suzy Sparkle were singers in
a band called Jewels. They sang all over the
land from Aberdeen to Penzance but one Monday the other
singers in the band left. Danny and Suzy were very unhappy.
Then their car broke down and they had to walk in the rain.
They saw a school and went in to ask the teachers for help.
The children were singing in class. "Wow!" said Danny.
"These children should join our band!"

Proper nouns	Common nouns
Danny Dazzle	*singers*
Suzy Sparkle	

Teaching objective: Y3 T1 S1 *common and proper nouns; grammatical awareness*

Name ....

The Great Whatsit

Change the common nouns into proper nouns to make two different sentences.

Example: The <u>man</u> drove off in his <u>car</u>.
1 Freddie Flash drove off in his Ferrari.
2 Mr Moneybags drove off in his Rolls Royce.

The girl wore new trainers.

1 ....

2 ....

The dog ate the food.

1 ....

2 ....

The woman went to the city.

1 ....

2 ....

The pirate sailed a ship.

1 ....

2 ....

Teaching objective: Y3 T1 S1 *common and proper nouns; grammatical awareness*

Name ....

Alphie's Action Alphabet

Write the correct verb under each picture of Alphie. Choose from the box.

attacks	zooms	quivers	limps	hops	explores
races	digs	balances	kicks	scratches	yelps

....

....

....

Teaching objective: Y3 T1 S3,5 *verbs*

Name ....

Alphie's Action Alphabet

Spot the verbs and underline them.

One day as Alphie trotted by a toy shop he saw a big basket of teddies outside the shop door. Alphie took one.

He stuck his nose in the basket, opened his mouth wide, grabbed a bear and crept away – but the shopkeeper saw Alphie and rushed out of the shop. Down the street Alphie raced with the shopkeeper behind him.

Alphie saw a bush and crept under it to hide. "I hope nobody finds me," thought the bad dog. But the teddy was a talking teddy.

First it squeaked. Alphie shook with surprise.

Then it growled – and Alphie shivered with fear.

Then the teddy roared.

Alphie yelped and jumped straight out of the bush.

"Got you!" said the shopkeeper. "And I've got my teddy back too."

Teaching objective: Y3 T1 S3,5 *verbs*

Name ....

Alphie's Action Alphabet

Underline all the verbs and verb phrases.

Alphie likes everyone. He even likes Killer – the cat next door.

Killer always hisses and spits at Alphie – and he sometimes eats

Alphie's dinner.

One day Killer the cat was annoying Alphie. He scratched

Alphie's nose and jumped on to Alphie's back. Alphie howled

and yelped. His nose was hurting! He ran to the garden pond

and plunged his nose into the cool water. Killer squealed and fell

off Alphie's back. Splash! Killer and Alphie tumbled into the

pond. Alphie swam around happily. He really enjoyed it – but

Killer did not!

Teaching objective: Y3 T1 S3,5 *verbs*

Name ....

Alphie's Action Alphabet

*Write a Monster Alphabet. Write a verb
for each letter of the alphabet.*

My monster acts.

My monster b..

My monster c..

My monster d..

My monster e..

My monster f..

My monster g..

My monster h..

My monster imagines.

My monster j..

My monster k..

My monster l..

My monster m..

My monster n..

My monster overbalances.

My monster p..

My monster quacks.

My monster r..

My monster s..

My monster t..

My monster understands.

My monster v..

My monster w..

My monster explores.

My monster y..

My monster z..

Teaching objective: Y3 T1 S3,5 *verbs*

Name ....

What the animals said

Change each said *to a powerful verb.*

"Stop!" said the elephant.

"Look out!" said the lion.

The hyena giggled and said, "Oh no!"

The mouse said, "Take your time!"

The crocodile sighed and said, "Please stop!"

"Take care!" the hippo said.

"Hmmmm, hmmmm!" said the hummingbirds.

The monkeys chattered and muttered.

But the snake said, "I shall not be stopped!"

And over the edge of the cliff he dropped.

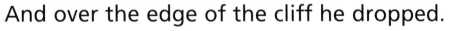

Teaching objective: Y3 T1 S3,5 *powerful verbs*

Name ....

What the animals said

Change each went *to a powerful verb.*

The elephants went through the bushes.

The lion went through the grass.

The hyenas went into the woods.

The mouse went under a leaf.

The crocodile went into the river.

The hippo went into the lake.

The hummingbirds went high in the sky.

The monkey went up the trees.

But the snake went – over the edge of the cliff.

Teaching objective: Y3 T1 S3,5 *powerful verbs*

Name ....

What the animals said

Change each **went,** **said** *and* **got**
phrase to a powerful verb.
The first one is done for you.

crashed
The elephants ~~went~~ through the bushes

We must
and said, "~~We've got t~~o get there soon!"

The lion went through the grass and said, "In no

time we'll have got the snake."

The mouse went under a leaf. "I've got away!" she said.

The hippo went into the lake and said, "I got a bit too hot!"

The hummingbirds went high in the sky and said, "We got

much higher than you."

The monkey went up the trees and said, "I've got everything

I need."

But the snake went over the edge of the cliff. He got a bit

of a shock!

Teaching objective: Y3 T1 S3,5 *powerful verbs*

Big Book Grammar, Heinemann 2000. Copying permitted for purchasing school only. This material is not copyright free.

Name ....

Past and Present

Change all the past tense verbs into the present tense.

The Brick family lived in the present.

One night Mr and Mrs Brick were relaxing with the stars.

Mrs Brick heard a noise. "What was that?" she said.

They thought it might have been Snuggles. But he was asleep.

They got a torch and went outside, but they saw nothing unusual.

C-R-R-R-A-SH!

"That noise came from the kitchen!" said Mr and Mrs Brick.

They ran to find out what it could be.

It was just Baby Brick. He was looking for a drink.

Teaching objective: Y3 T1 S4 *tense*

Big Book Grammar, Heinemann 2000. Copying permitted for purchasing school only. This material is not copyright free.

Name ....

Past and Present

Change all the past tense verbs and verb phrases into the present tense.

The Rock family lived together happily. Sometimes Mrs Rock

made toys for Baby Rock. She tied some bones together and put

a pebble inside. Baby shook the bones and they rattled. The

baby loved his rattle.

One day Baby Rock lost his rattle. He crawled out of the cave

and looked for another toy. He found some stones and piled

them up. Then he found a hedgehog. He picked it up but it

curled into a tight spiky ball. "Ouch!" said Baby Rock and

dropped the hedgehog. The hedgehog

rolled towards the stones and knocked

them over.

Baby Rock had invented a new game.

He called it Prickles. He felt very proud

of his game. So did the hedgehog.

Teaching objective: Y3 T1 S4 *tense*

Name ....

Past and Present

Change these jokes into the present tense.

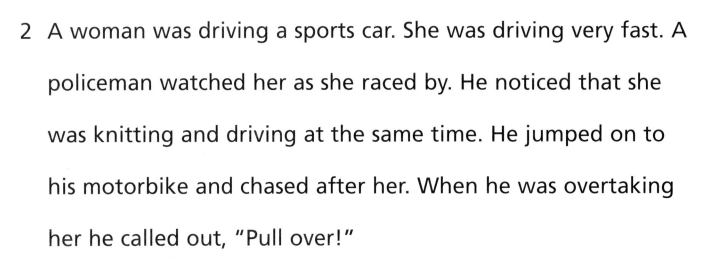

1 A man was sitting on a park bench.

He had a stick of rock in each ear.

A policeman came up to him and

asked him if he knew he had a stick

of rock in each ear.

"What were you saying?" asked

the man. "I couldn't hear you. I had rock in my ears."

2 A woman was driving a sports car. She was driving very fast. A

policeman watched her as she raced by. He noticed that she

was knitting and driving at the same time. He jumped on to

his motorbike and chased after her. When he was overtaking

her he called out, "Pull over!"

"No," the woman shouted back. "It's a scarf!"

Teaching objective: Y3 T1 S4 *tense*

Big Book Grammar, Heinemann 2000. Copying permitted for purchasing school only. This material is not copyright free.

Name ....

Past and Present

Change all the present tense verbs into the past tense.

The Rock family live in the past.

One night Mr and Mrs Rock are relaxing with the stars.

Mrs Rock hears a noise. "What is that?" she says.

They think it might be Snuggles. But he is asleep.

They get a torch and go outside, but they see nothing unusual.

C-R-R-R-A-SH!

"That noise comes from the kitchen!" say Mr and Mrs Rock.

They run to find out what it can be.

It is just Baby Rock. He is looking

for a drink.

Teaching objective: Y3 T1 S4 *tense*

Name ....

Past and Present

Change all the present tense verbs into the past tense.

The Brick family live together happily.

There is Mr Brick. There is Mrs Brick. There are the two

children and there is the baby. The Brick children like camping

holidays.

One day, they are camping by

the seaside. They explore and they

find a cave. They ask if they can go

in. Mr and Mrs Brick go in with

them - to make sure they are safe.

It is very dark. It smells old. Then

Baby Brick sees something. "Look! Look!" he says. "A rattle!"

"Silly Baby," says Mrs Brick. "You think it is a toy but it is just a

few old bones and a pebble."

The rest of the family agree that it is like a rattle. They

wonder where it is from.

Teaching objective: Y3 T1 S4 *tense*

Big Book Grammar, Heinemann 2000. Copying permitted for purchasing school only. This material is not copyright free.

Name ....

Past and Present

Change this joke into the past tense.

Ted has a job on a building site. He is very happy in his work. He sings and whistles all day. He works hard all morning then he goes for his dinner. He eats honey sandwiches and he drinks tea (with honey). Then he walks back to work. But when he arrives he sees that his tool bag has disappeared. Someone has stolen his hammer and his spade and his pick. Ted is very unhappy.

   This is the worst day of Ted's life. It is the day the teddy bear has his pick nicked.

Teaching objective: Y3 T1 S4 *tense*

Big Book Grammar, Heinemann 2000. Copying permitted for purchasing school only. This material is not copyright free.

Name ....

Knock knock!

Finish the jokes by putting in . ! or ?

Knock knock
Who's there
Boo
Boo who
Don't cry – it's only a joke

Knock knock
Who's there
Isabel
Isabel who
Isabel necessary on a bike

Knock knock
Who's there
Harry
Harry who
Harry up and open the door

How do you make an apple puff
Chase it round the kitchen

What's green and jumps round the garden
A spring onion

Practise reading the jokes with expression.
Pay attention to the punctuation.

Teaching objective: Y3 T1 S2,6 *question and exclamation marks*

Name ....

Knock knock!

Finish the jokes by putting in . ! or ?

Knock knock

Who's there

Lionel

Lionel who

Lionel bite you if you go too close

Knock knock

Who's there

Ivor

Ivor who

Ivor you open the door or I'll knock it down

Knock knock

Who's there

Twitter

Twitter who

I didn't know you could hoot like an owl

Knock knock

Who's there

Isabel

Isabel who

Isabel not better than all this silly knocking

What animal do you look like when you have a bath

A little bear

Practise reading the jokes with expression.

Pay attention to the punctuation.

Teaching objective: Y3 T1 S2,6 *question and exclamation marks*

Name ....

Knock knock!

Write some Knock knock! jokes of your own – or look some up in a joke book. Be sure to punctuate them properly by putting in . ! or ?

....

....

....

....

....

....

....

....

....

....

....

....

....

....

....

....

Teaching objective: Y3 T1 S2,6 *question and exclamation marks*

Name ....

The Seven Sentence Story

Put in full stops and capital letters to punctuate this story.
Then use coloured pens to highlight each sentence in a
different colour.

every year, Bertie the big-hearted
baker tried to win the baking
contest this year he had high
hopes for his delicious, squishy,
strawberry shortcake as he was
carrying the cake to the
competition, a car came swerving
round the corner it was heading
for a baby in a pushchair without
a thought for himself, Bertie
leapt out and pushed the child
to safety his strawberry shortcake
went spinning into the air fortunately the judges at the
competition awarded first prize to Bertie's extra-delicious,
extra-squishy, strawberry upside-down cake

Practise reading the story with expression.
Pay attention to the sentence boundaries.

Teaching objective: Y3 T1 S2,10,11,12 *sentences and sentence boundaries*

Name ....

The Seven Sentence Story

Punctuate this story. Put in full stops, capital letters and commas. Then use coloured pens to highlight each sentence in a different colour.

every year Betty the clumsy clodhopper hoped to win the dance contest she worked very hard and made a lovely new dress to wear unfortunately on the day of the contest she woke up very late Betty decided to run to the contest she did not see the banana skin on the steps into the room she slid on the banana tumbled over in the air spun around on the ground and slid on her nose towards the judges they awarded her first prize for her very unusual dance

Practise reading the story with expression. Pay attention to the sentence boundaries.

Teaching objective: Y3 T1 S2,10,11,12 *sentences and sentence boundaries*

Name ....

The Seven Sentence Story

On another piece of paper, write your own carefully punctuated seven sentence story. Write one sentence for each picture.

Teaching objective: Y3 T1 S2,10,11,12 *sentences and sentence boundaries*

Name ....

Chatterbox

Write the speeches in the speech balloons.

"What do you want to be when you grow up?" Chatterbox asked. "I'm going to be a footballer," Charley replied. "Great!" said Chatterbox.

"I bet you're going to be a cook when you grow up!" Chatterbox said. "Yeah!" answered Chad. "That's a brilliant job," agreed Chatterbox.

Teaching objective: Y3 T1 S7,8 *direct speech punctuation*

Chatterbox

Write the speeches in the speech bubbles.

Three fish saw a fishing line.

"A juicy worm!" said one.

"Don't bite it!" said the second.

"Yum!" said the third.

"Oh dear," said the first.

"They've got you," said the second.

"I've got him!" said number three and he pulled the fisherman into the lake.

Teaching objective: Y3 T1 S7,8 *direct speech punctuation*

Name ....

Chatterbox

Make up a story to go with these pictures. Write the speeches in the speech bubbles.

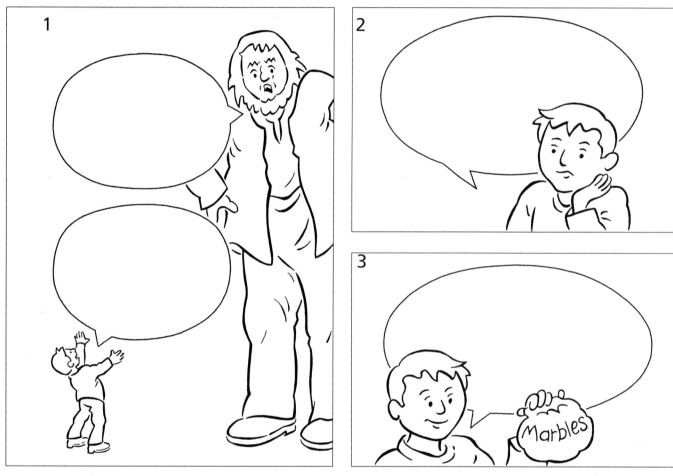

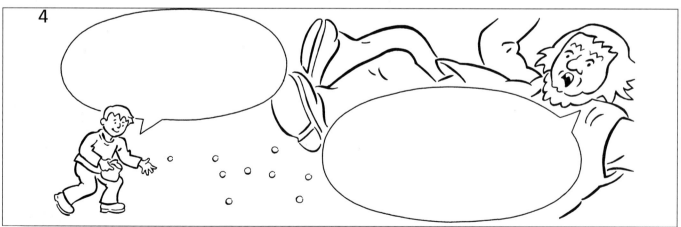

Teaching objective: Y3 T1 S7,8 *direct speech punctuation*

Name ....

Chatterbox

Put the speech from the speech balloons into direct speech.

> What do you want to be when you grow up?
>
> I'm going to be a footballer.
>
> Great!

" ....
....?" asked Chatterbox.

" ....," said Charley.

" ....
....!" Chatterbox smiled.

> I bet you're going to be a cook when you grow up!
>
> Yeah!
>
> That's a brilliant job.

" ....
....!" Chatterbox exclaimed.

" ....!" said Chad.

" ....
...." said Chatterbox.

Teaching objective: Y3 T1 S7,8 *direct speech punctuation*

Name ....

Chatterbox

Write the speeches from the speech bubbles as direct speech.
The boy's name is Billy and the man is his dad.

....

....

....

....

....

....

Teaching objective: Y3 T1 S7,8 *direct speech punctuation*

Name ....

Chatterbox

Write speeches in the speech bubbles. Then, on another piece of paper, write a story to go with these pictures. Include the speech bubble speech as direct speech.

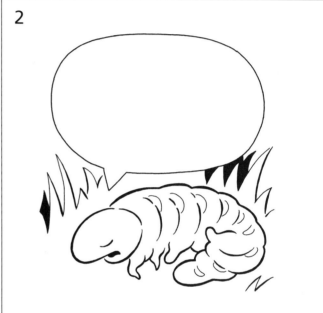

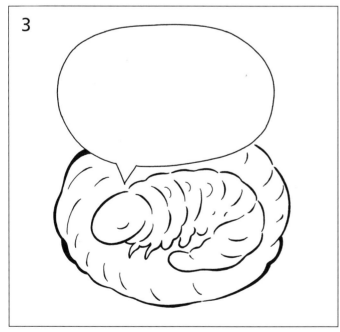

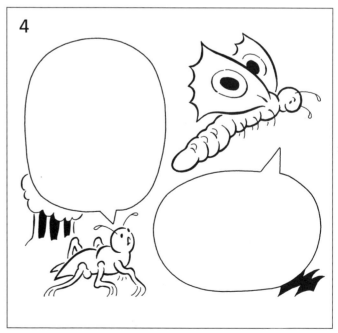

Teaching objective: Y3 T1 S7,8 *direct speech punctuation*

Name ....

The Punctuation Times

Mark the end of every sentence with a full stop, an exclamation mark or a question mark. Put a capital letter at the beginning of every sentence.

DR DOT'S QUEST COMES TO A FULL STOP

how many ways can you finish a sentence ☐ Dr Dorothea Dot, the famous explorer, has travelled the world to find out ☐ she claims there are only three ☐

Dr Dot points out that full stops, exclamation marks and question marks all have something in common ☐ "In a way they are all full stops ☐ the question and exclamation marks have an extra bit at the top, to show the tone of voice you should read in ☐ but the full stop is there at the bottom every time ☐"

APOSTROPHE STANDS IN FOR MISSING LETTERS

do you worry about where to put the apostrophe in shortened forms of words ☐ now Alec Smart, an eight-year-old schoolboy from Dorset, has the answer ☐ "It seems the apostrophe always goes where the letters have been missed out," explains Alec ☐ will Alec's formula always work ☐ can you find any exceptions ☐

Teaching objectives: Y3 T1 S2,6,10,11,12 *sentence punctuation;* Y3 T2 W15 *apostrophe in shortened forms*

Name ....

The Punctuation Times

Mark the end of every sentence with a full stop, an exclamation mark or a question mark.

Put a capital letter at the start of every sentence.

did you know that elephants love to swim they use their trunks as snorkels elephants live in herds and eat plants and trees

there are two sorts of elephants african elephants have big ears which they flap to keep cool indian elephants have smaller ears elephants can live for seventy years they are the largest land animal alive today

Write three sentences of your own about elephants. One should end with a full stop, one with a question mark and one with an exclamation mark.

....

....

....

Teaching objectives: Y3 T1 S2,6,10,11,12 *sentence punctuation;* Y3 T2 W15 *apostrophe in shortened forms*

Big Book Grammar, Heinemann 2000. Copying permitted for purchasing school only. This material is not copyright free.

Name ....

The Punctuation Times

Mark the end of every sentence with a full stop, an exclamation mark or a question mark.

Put a capital letter
- *at the start of every sentence*
- *for proper nouns.*

did you know you are not
allowed to keep a hamster as a
pet in australia the australians
worry that pet hamsters might
escape and become pests
hamsters make good pets they
live for about two years and
eat nuts and seeds they also
like fruit hamsters have sharp front teeth which keep growing
if a hamster is not given hard food to chew on, its teeth
would grow very long indeed

never keep two hamsters together in the same cage they will
fight they might even kill each other

*On another piece of paper write three sentences of your own
about hamsters. One should end with a full stop, one with a
question mark and one with an exclamation mark.*

Teaching objectives: Y3 T1 S2,6,10,11,12 *sentence punctuation*; Y3 T2 W15 *apostrophe in shortened forms*

Big Book Grammar, Heinemann 2000. Copying permitted for purchasing school only. This material is not copyright free.

Name ....

The Punctuation Times

In each underlined word an apostrophe has been missed out. Rewrite the word and put in the missing apostrophe. The first one has been done for you.

Cinderella was crying. She ~~couldnt~~ *couldn't* go to the ball. Her sisters

wouldnt let her go.

"I wish they werent always so mean to me," Cinderella

sobbed. "They shouldnt treat me the way they do. They really

shouldnt. Theyre never kind to me."

Just then there was a flash and

the Fairy Godmother appeared.

"You neednt cry any more," said

the fairy. "You dont need to be

unhappy. You can go to the ball!"

"I cant," said Cinderella. "I dont

have a coach. Ill just stay here. I wont go."

Teaching objectives: Y3 T1 S2,6,10,11,12 *sentence punctuation;* Y3 T2 W15 *apostrophe in shortened forms*

Big Book Grammar, Heinemann 2000. Copying permitted for purchasing school only. This material is not copyright free.

Name ....

The Punctuation Times

In each underlined word an apostrophe has been missed out. Rewrite the word and put in the missing apostrophe. The first one has been done for you.

"I want everybody to dive in today," said

the swimming teacher. "You ~~will not~~ *won't* have

any problems. You <u>cannot</u> hurt yourself."

"I <u>do not</u> think I can do it," said one boy.

"I <u>cannot</u> do it. I <u>have not</u> got the nerve."

"<u>Do not</u> worry," said the teacher. "You <u>should not</u> find it hard.

<u>You have</u> practised before. I <u>would not</u> ask you to do it if I <u>did not</u>

know you could do it easily. Be brave!"

"I <u>cannot</u>!" said the boy. "I <u>shall not</u>! I <u>will not</u>! <u>It is</u> not possible!"

The teacher sighed. "Well, you <u>need not</u> do it if you really

<u>have not</u> the nerve today. Perhaps you could do it tomorrow?"

"I <u>could not</u>!" said the boy. "It <u>would not</u> be a good idea!"

"Why not?" sighed the teacher.

"Because tomorrow the swimming pool is shut," said the boy.

"There <u>will not</u> be any water in the pool!"

Teaching objectives: Y3 T1 S2,6,10,11,12 *sentence punctuation*; Y3 T2 W15 *apostrophe in shortened forms*

Big Book Grammar, Heinemann 2000. Copying permitted for purchasing school only. This material is not copyright free.

Name ....

The Punctuation Times

How many shortened forms of words can you make in this passage? Put in the missing apostrophes. The first one is done to show you how.

Kit and Kat ~~could not~~ *couldn't* agree about anything.

"I am brilliant at spelling," said Kit. "I can spell anything! It is easy."

"No you cannot!" said Kat. "You are a really bad speller!"

"I will show you how good I am," said Kit.

"No you will not," said Kat. "I know you are not a good speller."

"So," said Kit, "you do not believe I can spell anything?"

"Right," said Kat. "I am sure you cannot spell anything."

"Well, listen to this," said Kit. "You will see!"

Kit spelled, "A N Y T H I N G. You see," Kit said. "I am a brilliant speller, are not I?"

Teaching objectives: Y3 T1 S2,6,10,11,12 *sentence punctuation*; Y3 T2 W15 *apostrophe in shortened forms*

Big Book Grammar, Heinemann 2000. Copying permitted for purchasing school only. This material is not copyright free.

Name ....

Adjectives for Sale!

Match the adjectives to the product.

disgusting

slimy

sporty

comfy

bright

warm

crispy

salty

cool

refreshing

friendly

cuddly

....

....

....

....

Teaching objective: Y3 T2 S2,3 *adjectives*

Name ....

Adjectives for Sale!

Match the adjectives to the product.

speedy

delicious

fast

creamy

sparkling

tiny

smelly

old

precious

small

huge

enormous

....

....

....

....

....

....

....

....

....

....

Teaching objective: Y3 T2 S2,3 *adjectives*

Name ....

Adjectives for Sale!

Write as many adjectives as you can to describe each of these things.

....
....
....

....
....
....

....
....
....

....
....
....

....
....
....

....
....
....

Teaching objective: Y3 T2 S2,3 *adjectives*

Name ....

Me and my Monster

Add adjectives to this menu.

Menu for me!

.... sausages

on a bed of

.... mash

....

pizza pieces

.... chips

.... salad

.... bananas

with .... cream

.... mints

Teaching objective: Y3 T1 S3,5 *adjectives*

Big Book Grammar, Heinemann 2000. Copying permitted for purchasing school only. This material is not copyright free.

Name ....

Me and my Monster

Add adjectives to this menu.

Menu for my monster!

.... sausages

on a bed of

.... mildewed mash

....

pizza pieces

.... chips

.... salad

(with extra slugs)

.... bananas

with .... cream

.... mints

Teaching objective: Y3 T1 S3,5 *adjectives*

Big Book Grammar, Heinemann 2000. Copying permitted for purchasing school only. This material is not copyright free.

Name ....

Me and my Monster

Add adjectives to describe these clothes. Make them sound good enough to buy!

Teaching objective: Y3 T1 S3,5 *adjectives*

Name ....

Me and my Monster

Add adjectives to describe these clothes. Make them disgusting!

Teaching objective: Y3 T1 S3,5 *adjectives*

Name ....

Me and my Monster

Imagine you are getting dressed in the best clothes you can think of and going to the best tea party in the world. Write the story. Use lots of interesting adjectives!

I was dressed in my best clothes.

I was wearing ....

....

....

....

....

....

....

....

....

....

....

....

"Yum!" I said. "That was delicious. Is there any more?"

Teaching objective: Y3 T1 S3,5 *adjectives*

Name ....

Me and my Monster

Write a story about the monster getting dressed and going out
for a monster tea. Use lots of interesting adjectives!

Mildew the monster was dressed
in her party best. She was wearing

....

....

....

....

....

....

....

....

....

....

....

....

"Yuk!" said Mildew. "That was delicious. Is there any more?"

Teaching objective: Y3 T1 S3,5 *adjectives*

Big Book Grammar, Heinemann 2000. Copying permitted for purchasing school only. This material is not copyright free.

Name ....

Singular and Plural

Put in the plurals.

A singular boy with a singular toy,

Plural .... with plural ....

A singular fox in a singular box,

Plural .... in plural ....

A singular witch in a singular ditch,

Plural .... in plural ....

A singular lady with a singular baby,

Plural .... with plural ....

A singular man with a singular mop,

Plural .... with plural ....

A singular drip and a singular drop,

Plural .... and plural ....

Teaching objectives: Y3 T2 S4,5 *singular and plural*; Y3 T2 S11 *grammatical agreement*

Name ....

Singular and Plural

Change the underlined singular nouns into the plural. The first one has been done for you.

There were once three little ~~dog~~ *dogs*. They were all very hungry.

   "I want to eat <u>bone</u>," said the first dog.

   "I want to eat <u>biscuit</u>," said the second dog.

   "I want to eat <u>chip</u>," said the third.

They went off to find food. Outside a shop they saw a pile of <u>box</u>, filled

with <u>apple</u> and <u>cornflake</u> and ice <u>lolly</u>. The <u>dog</u> licked their <u>lip</u> and stared

at the feast.

   "We mustn't touch it," sighed the first dog. "It doesn't belong to us –

and anyway there are some <u>policeman</u> on the corner."

   Then round the corner came two very strange <u>lady</u>. They were both

dressed in black and they were both wearing very funny <u>hat</u>.

   "Are they <u>witch</u>?" wondered the second dog. But they weren't <u>witch</u>.

They were just <u>lady</u> who had forgotten their shopping.

   "Look!" said one of the <u>lady</u>. "These <u>dog</u> have looked after our

shopping. Let's give them a reward."

   The <u>lady</u> gave the <u>dog</u> <u>bone</u> and <u>biscuit</u> and <u>chip</u> – lots and lots of <u>chip</u>.

Teaching objectives: Y3 T2 S4,5 *singular and plural*; Y3 T2 S11 *grammatical agreement*

Name ....

Singular and Plural

In this story some of the nouns need to be changed into the plural. Can you find them and correct them? The first one has been done for you.

There were once three little ~~dog~~ *dogs*. They were all very hungry.

"I want to eat bone," said the first dog.

"I want to eat biscuit," said the second dog.

"I want to eat chip," said the third.

They went off to find food. Outside a shop they saw a pile of box. They were filled with apple and cornflake and ice lolly. The dog licked their lip and stared at the feast.

"We mustn't touch it," sighed the first dog. "It doesn't belong to us – and anyway there are some policeman on the corner."

Then round the corner came two very strange lady. They were both dressed in black and they were both wearing very funny hat.

"Are they witch?" wondered the second dog. But they weren't witch. They were just lady who had forgotten their shopping.

"Look!" said one of the lady. "These dog have looked after our shopping. Let's give them a reward."

The lady gave the dog bone and biscuit and chip – lots and lots of chip.

Teaching objectives: Y3 T2 S4,5 *singular and plural*; Y3 T2 S11 *grammatical agreement*

Big Book Grammar, Heinemann 2000. Copying permitted for purchasing school only. This material is not copyright free.

Name ....

Singular and Plural

Change the underlined plural words into the singular. You may have to add some words sometimes. The first one has been done for you.

1 The ~~babies were~~ *baby was* crying.

2 Put the <u>books</u> in the <u>boxes</u>.

3 The <u>men</u> took the <u>dogs</u> into the <u>parks</u>.

4 <u>Divers</u> <u>swim</u> in the deep <u>seas</u>.

5 The <u>bears</u> <u>like</u> honey.

6 <u>Dinosaurs</u> <u>live</u> in the <u>swamps</u>.

7 The <u>swimmers were</u> afraid of the <u>sharks</u>.

8 The <u>machines</u> <u>have</u> <u>switches</u> and <u>buttons</u>.

Teaching objectives: Y3 T2 S4,5 *singular and plural*; Y3 T2 S11 *grammatical agreement*

Singular and Plural

Change the underlined plural words into the singular. You may have to add some words sometimes. The first one has been done for you.

One mouse
~~Two mice~~ lived in a wood. There was

no food left for <u>them</u> – not even

<u>nuts</u> or <u>berries</u>. So <u>they</u> left <u>their</u>

<u>homes</u> and went into a house to

look for food. <u>They</u> looked

everywhere. <u>They</u> looked in

<u>cupboards</u>, in <u>dustbins</u> and in <u>boxes</u>.

While <u>they</u> <u>were</u> looking, <u>they</u> found

old <u>dolls</u> and <u>teddies</u> but <u>they</u> could not find any food. All the

time, <u>they</u> <u>were</u> chased by <u>dogs</u>.

   "That gives <u>us</u> an idea!" said the <u>mice</u>. "If the <u>dogs</u> <u>are</u>

chasing <u>us</u>, <u>they</u> won't be looking after <u>their</u> food."

   The <u>mice</u> sneaked into the <u>kennels</u> and found <u>two</u> <u>bowls</u> of

dog food. <u>They</u> ate it all up.

Teaching objectives: Y3 T2 S4,5 *singular and plural*; Y3 T2 S11 *grammatical agreement*

Name ....

Singular and Plural

Change this story about two mice and two dogs into a story about one mouse and one dog. The first change has been done for you.

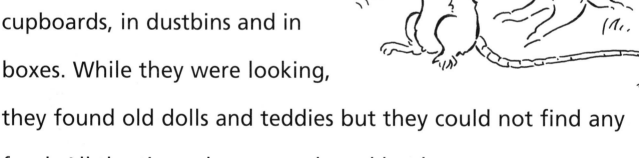

A mouse
~~Two mice~~ lived in a wood. There was no food left for them – not even nuts or berries. So they left their homes and went into a house to look for food. They looked everywhere. They looked in cupboards, in dustbins and in boxes. While they were looking, they found old dolls and teddies but they could not find any food. All the time, they were chased by dogs.

"That gives us an idea!" said the mice. "If the dogs are chasing us, they won't be looking after their food."

The mice sneaked into the kennels and found two bowls of dog food. They ate it all up.

Teaching objectives: Y3 T2 S4,5 *singular and plural*; Y3 T2 S11 *grammatical agreement*

Name ....

All Together Now!

Write the correct collective noun under each picture.

pack	bunch	school	flock

team	pride	litter	herd

A .... of lions

A .... of whales

A .... of pups

A .... of horses

A .... of sheep

A .... of cows

A .... of wolves

A .... of bananas

Teaching objectives: Y3 T2 S4,5 *collective nouns*; Y3 T2 S11 *grammatical agreement*

Name ....

All Together Now!

Match the correct collective noun to the picture. The first one has been done for you. Use a dictionary to help.

galaxy	nest	herd	class

gaggle	pack	swarm	fleet

A herd of cows

....

....

....

....

....

....

Teaching objectives: Y3 T2 S4,5 *collective nouns*; Y3 T2 S11 *grammatical agreement*

Name ....

All Together Now!

The collective nouns have
been mixed up! Sort them out
and match them up. The first
one has been done for you.

A fleet of schoolchildren   *A class of schoolchildren*

A herd of bananas   ....

A bunch of stars   ....

A pack of mice   ....

A nest of lions   ....

A galaxy of cows   ....

A pride of sheep   ....

A flock of ships   ....

A class of wolves   ....

Teaching objectives: Y3 T2 S4,5 *collective nouns*; Y3 T2 S11 *grammatical agreement*

Name ....

All Together Now!

Make up your own collective nouns to go with the pictures.
The first one has been done for you.

A squidge of cream cakes

.... *of puddings*

.... *of worms*

.... *of monsters*

.... *of snakes*

.... *of toys*

.... *of butterflies*

Teaching objectives: Y3 T2 S4,5 *collective nouns*; Y3 T2 S11 *grammatical agreement*

Chunky Comma to the Rescue!

Use a coloured pen to put in the missing commas.

Once upon a time long before any of us were born in a country far from here a little old woman whose name was Madame Mandragora lived in a cottage by a singing stream and with her lived her faithful dog who was called Bonzo.

Dear Parents,

For the school trip your child will need a packed lunch pencil paper wellingtons sunscreen raincoat and no more than £1 spending money.

I like Baz who does yoyo tricks better than Bo.

Write a sentence of your own that needs two commas.

....

Teaching objectives: Y3 T2 S6,7 *uses of the comma*

Big Book Grammar, Heinemann 2000. Copying permitted for purchasing school only. This material is not copyright free.

Chunky Comma to the Rescue!

Use a coloured pen to put in the missing commas.

Long ago and faraway in a strange strange land called Ompopalop a very small old man whose name was Rimpytimp lived in a cave by the deep dark woods and with him lived a little cat an old grey rat and a goat as big as a carthorse who was called Sweetiepie.

Dear Children,

For the trip you will need: sleeping bag snacks paper wellingtons hat sunscreen pens warm socks and some spending money.

Our house which is on the High Street is seventy years old.

Write a sentence of your own that needs two commas.

Teaching objective: Y3 T2 S6,7 *uses of the comma*

Name ....

Chunky Comma to the Rescue!

Use a coloured pen to put in the missing commas, full stops and capital letters.

One day our class which is called blue class and has mrs simpson as the teacher went to the seaside we ate candy floss rock fish chips with vinegar ice-cream and lollies I dropped my lolly and it got covered in sand but mrs simpson bought me another after lunch we went on the roundabout the skyride and the roller coaster then it was time to go home on the bus on the way home gary sally barry and mrs simpson all said they felt a bit sick.

Write a sentence of your own that needs three commas.

....

Teaching objective: Y3 T2 S6,7 *uses of the comma*

Name ....

The Capital Wall

Use a coloured pen to put in the missing capital letters.

ben loves nikki
ps and
nikki loves ben

prospect players

present

**the importance of
being frank**

by frank wilde

fri – sat – sun 2nd, 3rd, 4th march

✪

starring: sir john feelgood

tom pants

gwyneth poultry

sharon rock

sold out

*capital letters are
bigger and better,
they show where a
sentence begins.
they give to a name
an aura of fame
by starting it off
with a swing*

holiday in italy
come to rome or milan
flights every tuesday in april

contact your local travel agent:
mr i bookham, 9 airport road, stansted

Teaching objective: Y3 T2 S8 *uses of capital letters*

Big Book Grammar, Heinemann 2000. Copying permitted for purchasing school only. This material is not copyright free.

Name ....

The Capital Wall

Use a coloured pen to put in the missing capital letters.

lost

small black and white dog called **alphie**.
good at tricks.
our cat, killer, misses him.

if found, please return to:
trevor bunton
dog lane, barking

---

all welcome

On tuesday, september 3rd
Class 3 will present their play

the lion who ate my socks

✪

starring: leo wallace felicity stocking
amina sawalha declan o'hara

---

there was a young man
of bengal
who went to a fancy
dress ball,
he went just for fun,
dressed up as a bun,
and a dog ate him up
in the hall.

---

holiday in spain

come to ibiza or malaga
flights every saturday in june

contact your local travel agent:
mr ivor ticket, 9 runway lane, luton

Teaching objective: Y3 T2 S8 *uses of capital letters*

Name ....

The Capital Wall

Use a coloured pen to put in the missing capital letters.

albert wiffle went to newtown library and took out three books they were james and the giant peach by roald dahl, the famous five have another picnic by enid blyton and a new book called the dogs' dinner by nora bone.

then he went home to his little house on high street and watched television his favourite programmes are westenders and green peter.

albert's grandmother, mrs eugenia wiffle, was nearly 103. her birthday was on 5th march, which this year was on a monday. albert had bought her a new mountain bike and a copy of how to cook by delia smith.

Teaching objective: Y3 T2 S8 *uses of capital letters*

Name ....

Teach Yourself Earth

Help the space creatures
by correcting the mistakes.

Creature 1: I ~~has~~ *have* been learning

English for three

weeks. My teacher are

very pleased with my progress, but she feel I needs to

practise. You is learning English too, I thinks?

Creature 2: Yes, I is learning English also. I likes English. I has also

learned how to eat Earth food. I puts it up my nose

and twists my ear three times. That do the trick – yum!

Creature 1: Has you eaten many interesting foods?

Creature 2: Yes, I has eaten spiders, lampposts and bobble hats.

The bobble hats was particularly delicious.

Creature 1: Ah, we doesn't have food like this at home. These

Earth people has such a variety. Isn't they lucky?

Teaching objective: Y3 T2 S10,11 *1st/2nd/3rd person agreement*

Name ....

Teach Yourself Earth

Help the space creatures by correcting the mistakes.

Creature 2:   And another thing I *have* ~~has~~ learned is how to roller skate.

I just puts this thing on my head and off I goes. Is you watching?

Creature 1:   That are very impressive. You goes very fast. But do it not hurt when you crash into things?

Creature 2:   I usually wears this protective clothing, which help a lot.

Creature 1:   Well, that were a very interesting conversation. I is off for my next lesson – Lesson 123. Is you coming?

Creature 2:   Yes. But what we really needs is some people who speaks English to help us. I wonders if there are anybody out there...?

Teaching objective: Y3 T2 S10,11 *1st/2nd/3rd person agreement*

Name ....

Teach Yourself Earth

Help the space creatures by correcting the mistakes.

Creature 1:   What ~~does~~ *do* these Earth people does every day? I is keen

to know all about them.

Creature 2:   They does strange things. Has you not watched them?

They splashes water all over and they puts fresh

coverings on their bodies. Then they goes off in little

tin boxes with wheels. They goes to school.

Creature 1:   I goes to school too. What does they does at school?

Creature 2:   They gets things called books. Then they makes little

marks on paper. They calls it reading and writing.

Creature 1:   I has seen that. What does they does at the end of

the day?

Creature 2:   They gets into things called beds. Then they switches

themselves off and lies in the dark for a long time.

Then they gets up and starts again.

Creature 1:   I is glad I is not an earth person.

Teaching objective: Y3 T2 S10,11 *1st/2nd/3rd person agreement*

Name ....

The Village without Pronouns

Change all the underlined words to pronouns.

Once upon a time there was a village where the villagers had a particular problem. An ogre ruled over <u>the villagers</u> and the <u>ogre</u> had snaffled all <u>the villagers'</u> pronouns. Now whenever <u>the villagers</u> talked or wrote letters or stories, <u>the villagers</u> had to use lots of extra words. Speaking and writing can be tricky when <u>speakers and writers</u> do not have pronouns.

"What can <u>the villagers</u> do about the problem?" the villagers wondered.

"<u>The villagers</u> must go to the ogre's store," said Heggetty." <u>The villagers</u> must find the pronouns and set <u>the pronouns</u> free. Follow m… <u>Heggetty</u>!"

"<u>The villagers</u> will follow <u>Heggetty</u>!" the villagers cried. "For <u>the villagers</u> are fed up with talking in this silly way."

Teaching objective: Y3 T3 S3 *personal and possessive pronouns*

Name ....

The Village without Pronouns

Change all the underlined words to pronouns.

The ogre lived with <u>the ogre's</u> mum in the castle near the village.

The ogre was scared of <u>the ogre's</u> mum because <u>the ogre's mum</u>

was even bigger than <u>the ogre</u> was. <u>The ogre's mum</u> was also

noisier, nastier, and <u>the ogre's mum</u> nagged.

   "When will <u>the ogre</u> ever learn to behave properly?"

<u>the ogre's mum</u> said to the ogre. "<u>The ogre's mum</u> has spent all

day cooking this flock of sheep

for <u>the ogre</u> and <u>the ogre</u> only

ate twelve of <u>the sheep</u>.

<u>The ogre</u> will never grow big

and strong if <u>the ogre</u> doesn't

eat all <u>the ogre's</u> dinner!"

When you have changed the ogre's mum's speech read it aloud.
Find two verbs that need changing and put them right.

Teaching objective: Y3 T3 S3 *personal and possessive pronouns*

Name ....

The Village without Pronouns

Correct this passage by putting in pronouns where they are needed. The first one has been done for you.

The ogre lived with ~~the ogre's~~ *his* mum in the castle near the village.

The ogre was scared of the ogre's mum because the ogre's mum

was even bigger than the ogre was. The ogre's mum was also

noisier, nastier, and the ogre's

mum nagged.

"When will the ogre ever

learn to behave properly?" the

ogre's mum said to the ogre.

"The ogre's mum has spent all

day cooking this flock of sheep

for the ogre and the ogre only ate twelve of the sheep. The ogre

will never grow big and strong if the ogre doesn't eat all the

ogre's dinner!"

When you have changed the ogre's mum's speech read it aloud.
Find two verbs that need changing and put them right.

Teaching objective: Y3 T3 S3 *personal and possessive pronouns*

The Village without Pronouns

Put the pronouns into their correct pot.

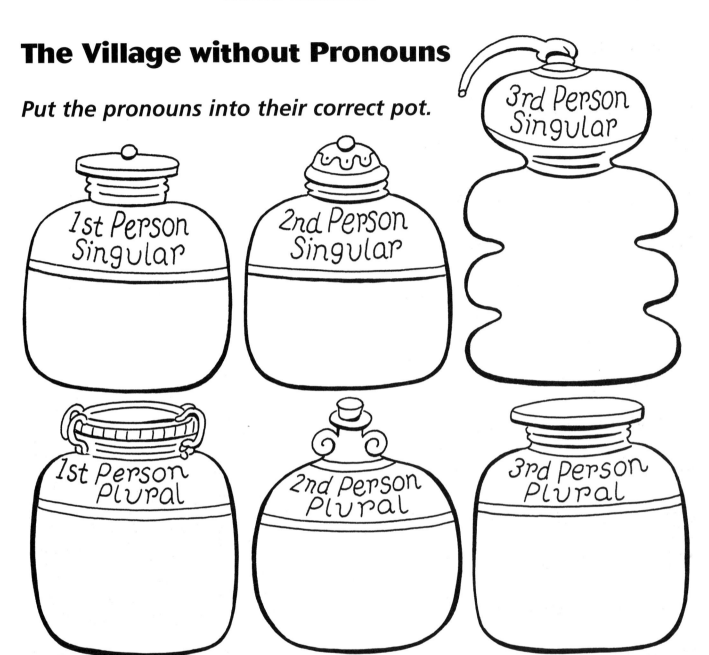

ours   him   yourselves   mine   it   yourself   them   we

herself   their   his   I   ourselves   yours   its   she   you

myself   yours   themselves   he   my   himself   hers

her   our   your   theirs   me   itself   your   they   us

Teaching objective: Y3 T3 S3 *personal and possessive pronouns*

Name ....

Links are Us!

Cut out the short sentences and conjunctions at the bottom of the page.

Try different ways of joining the sentences to make sense. You can use a conjunction at the beginning of the sentence or in the middle. Write out six sentences that make sense.

1. ....

2. ....

3. ....

4. ....

5. ....

6. ....

| Norman was boring | whenever | when |
| the animals went to sleep | so | because |

✂

Teaching objectives: Y3 T3 S5 *conjunctions*; Y3 T3 S7 *commas marking grammatical boundaries*

Big Book Grammar, Heinemann 2000. Copying permitted for purchasing school only. This material is not copyright free.

Name ....

Links are Us!

Cut out the short sentences and conjunctions at the bottom of the page.

Try different ways of joining the sentences to make sense. You can use a conjunction at the beginning of the sentence or in the middle. Write out six sentences that make sense.

1. ....

2. ....

3. ....

4. ....

5. ....

6. ....

| Matilda was frightened | whenever | so |
| the bear roared loudly | because | when |

Teaching objectives: Y3 T3 S5 *conjunctions*; Y3 T3 S7 *commas marking grammatical boundaries*

Big Book Grammar, Heinemann 2000. Copying permitted for purchasing school only. This material is not copyright free.

Name ....

Links are Us!

Make up a sentence in two parts using one of the conjunctions at the bottom of the page.

Write the two parts of your sentence in the strips provided. Cut them out and try linking the strips in different ways, using different conjunctions and different orders.

| when | because | so | whenever |

On another piece of paper, write a selection of the best sentences you make.

Teaching objectives: Y3 T3 S5 *conjunctions*; Y3 T3 S7 *commas marking grammatical boundaries*

Name ....

Links are Us!

Cut out the short sentences and conjunctions at the bottom of the page. Try different ways of joining the sentences to make sense. You can use a conjunction at the beginning of the sentence or in the middle. Write out the sentences and don't forget to start with a capital letter and end with a full stop.

1. ....

2. ....

3. ....

4. ....

5. ....

6. ....

7. ....

8. ....

9. ....

10. ....

| Mr Smith was busy | since | so | whenever |
| class B worked quietly | because | while | if |

Teaching objectives: Y3 T3 S5 *conjunctions*; Y3 T3 S7 *commas marking grammatical boundaries*

Big Book Grammar, Heinemann 2000. Copying permitted for purchasing school only. This material is not copyright free.

Name ....

Links are Us!

Cut out the short sentences and conjunctions at the bottom of the page. Try different ways of joining the sentences to make sense. You can use a conjunction at the beginning of the sentence or in the middle. Write out the sentences and don't forget to start with a capital letter and end with a full stop.

1. ....

2. ....

3. ....

4. ....

5. ....

6. ....

7. ....

8. ....

9. ....

10. ....

the sun was shining	because	so	if	since
whenever	while	the children were happy		

✂

Teaching objectives: Y3 T3 S5 *conjunctions*; Y3 T3 S7 *commas marking grammatical boundaries*

Name ....

Links are Us!

Make up a sentence in two parts using any conjunction from the bottom of the page.

Write the two parts of your sentence in the strips provided. Cut them out and try linking the strips in different ways.

Then try linking them with the following conjunctions: because, when, so, whenever. *How many different sentences can you make?*

✄ ....

✄ ....

| if | since | while |

✄

On another piece of paper, write a selection of the best sentences you make.

Teaching objectives: Y3 T3 S5 *conjunctions*; Y3 T3 S7 *commas marking grammatical boundaries*

Big Book Grammar, Heinemann 2000. Copying permitted for purchasing school only. This material is not copyright free.

Name ....

Shrinking Violet

Choose the correct time connective from the list and complete the poem.

In school ...., Violet Henn
Was chewing on her felt tip pen.
.... Violet found
She was much closer to the ground.
.... she shrank to toddler size –
Her friends could not believe their eyes.
.... she shrank down even more,
To just six inches off the floor.
.... the teacher called for aid
From parents, police and fire brigade.
"Oh dear!" they cried. "What shall we do?"
But, very sadly, no one knew.
...., Violet was a dot
No bigger than a felt tip blot.
.... she was so small
That she could not be seen at all.
...., the teacher stood and sighed,
"Well, we have done our best. We tried.
.... we must learn from Violet Henn,
and NEVER chew a felt tip pen."

at last
one morning
meanwhile
all of a sudden
by lunchtime
first
then after lunch
next
now

Teaching objectives: Y3 T3 S6 *time connectives*; Y3 T3 S7 *commas marking grammatical boundaries*

Big Book Grammar, Heinemann 2000. Copying permitted for purchasing school only. This material is not copyright free.

Name ....

Shrinking Violet

Choose time connectives from the list to complete the Spider's Diary. Use a capital letter to start a new sentence.

I woke up early, ... started spinning.

I spun busily .... I had made a wonderful

web. .... a juicy fly came along.

.... it flew above the web.

.... it flew under the web.

.... it flew into the middle.

.... I waited quietly.

.... I had a little rest.

.... I will start my work again.

meanwhile	then	now
all of a sudden	until	next
first	at last	after lunch

Teaching objectives: Y3 T3 S6 *time connectives*; Y3 T3 S7 *commas marking grammatical boundaries*

Name ....

Shrinking Violet

Choose time connectives to complete the Spider's Diary.
Don't forget to use a capital letter to start a new sentence.

I woke up early, ... started spinning. I spun

busily .... I had made a wonderful web.

.... a juicy fly came along.

.... it flew above the web.

.... it flew under the web.

.... it flew into the

middle. .... I waited

quietly. .... I had a little rest.

.... I will start my work again.

Teaching objectives: Y3 T3 S6 *time connectives*; Y3 T3 S7 *commas marking grammatical boundaries*